P9-CDU-276

KRAZY KAT

KRAZY KAT

BY *Herriman*

WITH AN INTRODUCTION BY e. e. cummings

Madison Square Press

Grosset & Dunlap
A National General Company
PUBLISHERS NEW YORK

KREDITS

WRITTEN AND DRAWN
by George Herriman

INTRODUCTIONS
by e. e. cummings and Barbara Gelman

PRODUCED
by Woody Gelman and Nostalgia Press

RESEARCHED
by Dave Kaler, Ron Goulart and Ernie McGee

EDITED
by Joseph Greene and Rex Chessman

CAPTIONED
by Rex Chessman

ART
by Rick Varesi (Headings) and Lois Wallace (Mechanicals)

DESIGNED
by Woody Gelman

Copyright © 1969 by King Features Syndicate, Inc.,
Nostalgia Press, Inc., and Grosset & Dunlap, Inc.
Published simultaneously in Canada
Library of Congress Catalog Card No.: 74-89522
Printed in the United States of America
Copyright 1946, by e. e. cummings. Reprinted by
permission of the estate of e. e. cummings.

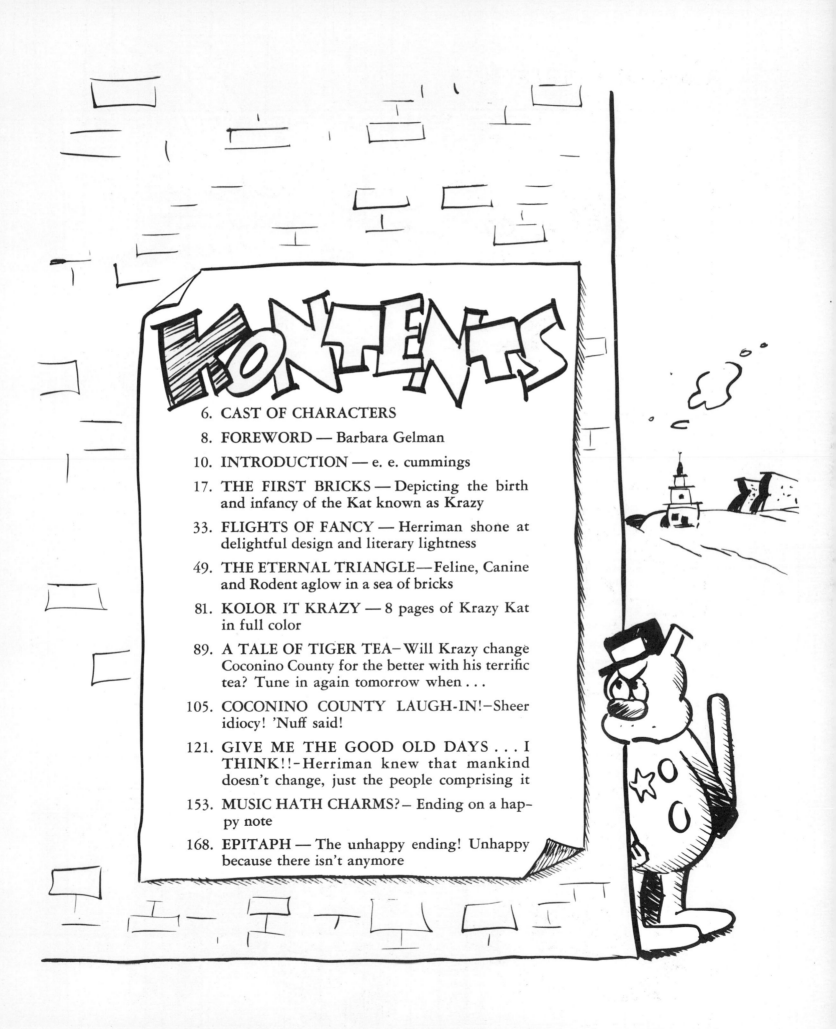

KONTENTS

6. CAST OF CHARACTERS

8. FOREWORD — Barbara Gelman

10. INTRODUCTION — e. e. cummings

17. THE FIRST BRICKS — Depicting the birth and infancy of the Kat known as Krazy

33. FLIGHTS OF FANCY — Herriman shone at delightful design and literary lightness

49. THE ETERNAL TRIANGLE — Feline, Canine and Rodent aglow in a sea of bricks

81. KOLOR IT KRAZY — 8 pages of Krazy Kat in full color

89. A TALE OF TIGER TEA — Will Krazy change Coconino County for the better with his terrific tea? Tune in again tomorrow when . . .

105. COCONINO COUNTY LAUGH-IN! — Sheer idiocy! 'Nuff said!

121. GIVE ME THE GOOD OLD DAYS . . . I THINK!! — Herriman knew that mankind doesn't change, just the people comprising it

153. MUSIC HATH CHARMS? — Ending on a happy note

168. EPITAPH — The unhappy ending! Unhappy because there isn't anymore

Cast of Characters

7

FOREWORD

Barbara Gelman

OF THE ALL-TIME GREATS OF THE COMIC STRIP, the most talked about—yet paradoxically the most difficult to talk about—is *Krazy Kat.* An army of luminaries, including Gilbert Seldes, e. e. cummings, and Deems Taylor, have tried to capture and define the elusive qualities of this comic strip. For one of the irresistible charms of George Herriman's wild little dream world was that the enthusiastic aficionado who "got it" felt that he had to explain it to others who were (obviously) incapable of understanding it his way. And each reader felt that he, and he alone, really got what *Krazy Kat* was all about.

But there is *no* explaining *Krazy Kat.* For all the allegorical, philosophical, political, meanings attributed to it by devoted readers, it was, and remains, primarily an experience, one to be had only at first hand.

The strip itself is based on the age-old lovers' triangle, but one with a peculiar and unexpected difference, for the triangle is a dog, a cat, and a mouse. Offissa Pupp, a very masculine canine, is crazy about Krazy, a cat of indeterminate gender (sometimes referred to as "she," but often as "he"), who is in turn mad about Ignatz Mouse, a male rodent who lives only to vent his hostility on Krazy by hurling bricks at her loving head. Ignatz will go to any lengths to find a brick to hurl at the head of Krazy. And Krazy lives to be beaned with that omnipresent brick. To our heroine—or hero—it is a sign that her "l'il angil" Ignatz is constant and true: "He neva fah-gets," as Krazy puts it. Her persistence in seeing the situation in her own way gives the strip its distinctive flavor. It also causes Offissa Pupp to love the innocent cat even more, and impassions him with an absolute determination to protect her from the vicious blows of Ignatz; but even he cannot fail to see, as the rest of us do, that those swiftly flying bricks are the prime source of Krazy's happiness.

Every day, for more than thirty years, this little drama was played, with endless variations, against the constantly shifting background of Coconino County, sparsely decorated with all manner of cacti and scrub, fire hydrants and bathtubs. As in any dream world, all things are possible in Coconino. At the drop of a panel, night could turn into day—and frequently did—and neither the characters nor the fans who "got it" ever blinked an eye.

But for every fan who "got" the mind-blowing symphony, there were probably fifty who never could figure out what this surrealistic little

cosmos was all about. In this respect *Krazy Kat* is as unique in the annals of success stories as it is in the history of comics. It may well be the most celebrated comic strip of all time, and it was probably considered the greatest even in its own time: Woodrow Wilson flatly refused to miss a single episode; dolls, books, and toys reflected the images of *Krazy Kat*, the slickest periodicals carried articles about the strip; and even a serious, if ill-fated, ballet was based on Herriman's creation. Still, *Krazy Kat* was never phenomenally popular. In the thirties, when such popular comic strips as *Blondie* were appearing daily in about a thousand newspapers, *Krazy Kat* was appearing in only thirty-five. And when the more popular cartoonists were earning upwards of $1,500 a week, Herriman was earning $750. Once, considering the revenue Krazy was bringing in, Herriman suggested to King Features that perhaps his salary was a bit high. But William Randolph Hearst, bossman of the syndicate and member pre-eminent of the society of Kat-lovers, gave orders that *Krazy Kat* was to go on for as long as Herriman wanted it to. Such was the fanatic loyalty of Kat-lovers. And such was the diffidence, integrity, and character of George Joseph Herriman.

Born in 1880 in New Orleans, the son of a baker, Herriman dropped out of high school and went to work in his father's bakery. He had already begun to draw, an activity which his father disapproved vehemently. Nonetheless, when George married in 1901, he decided to come to New York and try his hand at the cartoon markets. He sold cartoons to *Judge* and *Life*, drew political and sports cartoons for the New York *News* and *The World*, and worked on several strips—*Lariat Pete, Bud Smith*, and *Major Ozone.*

In 1908 Herriman went to work for Hearst and the New York *Journal*. There he began to draw a strip called *The Dingbat Family*, in which there appeared a rather fey family cat. The cat was soon joined by a mouse who had an unnerving, unrodentlike penchant for pursuing and torturing the cat. So began reality's reversal. It was to give birth to what may well be *the* classic among classics of comic art.

The Dingbat Family appeared for several years, the cat and mouse providing amusing, but minor, action on the floor and the trials and tribulations of the family the real action. But the weird relationship between cat and mouse became more and more amusing and overshadowed the Dingbats; by 1916 *Krazy Kat* had become a full-fledged, full-time comic strip all its own.

The rest is history. Garnering what was no doubt the most famous fan club in existence—each fan was a fan club of its own—*Krazy Kat* went on uninterrupted in its surrealistic, marvelously personal and private little world until the death of George Herriman in 1944.

The loss to Kat-lovers was great, but the strip has since become legend. Yet what is legend is never lost. And, dah-links, say da troof, among today's short-haired lasses and long-haired lads, with their emphasis on love, love, love, would not our she-he Kat, living in her-his cosmos untrammeled by time, space, and reality, be the Queen-King of Psychedelia?

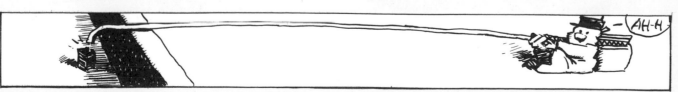

INTRODUCTION

e. e. cummings

TWENTY YEARS AGO, a celebration happened—the celebration of Krazy Kat by Gilbert Seldes. It happened in a book called *The Seven Lively Arts;* and it happened so wisely, so lovingly, so joyously, that recelebrating Krazy would be like teaching penguins to fly. Penguins (as a lot of people don't realize) do fly—not through the sea of the sky but through the sky of the sea—and my present ambition is merely, with our celebrated friend's assistance, to show how their flying affects every non-penguin.

What concerns me fundamentally is a meteoric burlesk melodrama, born of the immemorial adage *love will find a way.* This frank frenzy (encouraged by a strictly irrational landscape in perpetual metamorphosis) generates three protagonists and a plot. Two of the protagonists are easily recognized as a cynical brick-throwing mouse and a sentimental policeman-dog. The third protagonist—whose ambiguous gender doesn't disguise the good news that here comes our heroine—may be described as a humbly poetic, gently clownlike, supremely innocent, and illimitably affectionate creature (slightly resembling a child's drawing of a cat, but gifted with the secret grace and obvious clumsiness of a penguin on terra firma) who is never so happy as when egoist-mouse, thwarting altruist-dog, hits her in the head with a brick. Dog hates mouse and worships "cat," mouse despises "cat" and hates dog, "cat" hates no one and loves mouse.

Ignatz Mouse and Offissa Pupp are opposite sides of the same coin. Is Offissa Pupp kind? Only insofar as Ignatz Mouse is cruel. If you're a twofisted, spineless progressive (a mighty fashionable stance nowadays), Offissa

Pupp, who forcefully asserts the will of so-called society, becomes a cosmic angel; while Ignatz Mouse, who forcefully defies society's will by asserting his authentic own, becomes a demon of anarchy and a fiend of chaos. But if —whisper it—you're a 100% hidebound reactionary, the foot's in the other shoe. Ignatz Mouse then stands forth as a hero, pluckily struggling to keep the flag of free-will flying; while Offissa Pupp assumes the monstrous mien of a Goliath, satanically bullying a tiny but indomitable David. Well, let's flip the coin— so: and lo! Offissa Pupp comes up. That makes Ignatz Mouse "tails." Now we have a hero whose heart has gone to his head and a villain whose head has gone to his heart.

This hero and this villain no more understand Krazy Kat than the mythical denizens of a two-dimensional realm understand some three-dimensional intruder. The world of Offissa Pupp and Ignatz Mouse is a knowledgeable power-world, in terms of which our unknowledgeable heroine is powerlessness personified. The sensical law of this world is *might makes right,* the nonsensical law of our heroine is *love conquers all.* To put the oak in the acorn: Ignatz Mouse and Offissa Pupp (each completely convinced that his own particular brand of might makes right) are simple-minded. Krazy isn't—therefore, to Offissa Pupp and Ignatz Mouse, Krazy is. But if both our hero and our villain don't and can't understand our heroine, each of them can and each of them does misunderstand her differently. To our softheaded altruist, she is the adorably helpless incarnation of saintliness. To our hardhearted egoist, she is the puzzlingly indestructible embodiment of idiocy. The be-

nevolent overdog sees her as an inspired weakling. The malevolent undermouse views her as a born target. Meanwhile Krazy Kat, through this double misunderstanding, fulfills her joyous destiny.

Let's make no mistake about Krazy. A lot of people "love" because, and a lot of people "love" although, and a few individuals love. Love is something illimitable; and a lot of people spend their limited lives trying to prevent anything illimitable from happening to them. Krazy, however, is not a lot of people. Krazy is herself. Krazy is illimitable—she loves. She loves in the only way anyone can love: illimitably. She isn't morbid and she isn't long-suffering; she doesn't "love" someone because he hurts her and she doesn't "love" someone although he hurts her. She doesn't, moreover, "love" someone who hurts her. Quite the contrary: she loves someone who gives her unmitigated joy. How? By always trying his limited worst to make her unlove him, and always failing—not that our heroine is insensitive (for a more sensitive heroine never existed), but that our villain's every effort to limit her love with his unlove ends by a transforming of his limitation into her illimitability. If you're going to pity anyone, the last anyone to pity is our loving heroine, Krazy Kat. You might better pity that doggedly idolatrous imbecile, our hero; who policemanfully strives to protect his idol from catastrophic desecration at the paws of our iconoclastic villain—never suspecting that this very desecration becomes, through our transcending heroine, a consecration; and that this consecration reveals the ultimate meaning of existence. But the person to really pity (if really pity you

must) is Ignatz. Poor villain! All his malevolence turns to beneficence at contact with Krazy's head. By profaning the temple of altruism, alias law and order, he worships (entirely against his will) at the shrine of love.

I repeat: let's make no mistake about Krazy. Her helplessness, as we have just seen, is merely sensical—nonsensically she's a triumphant, not to say invincible, phenomenon. As for this invincible phenomenon's supposed idiocy, it doesn't even begin to fool nonsensical you and me. Life, to a lot of people, means either the triumph of mind over matter or the triumph of matter over mind; but you and I aren't a lot of people. We understand that, just as there is something—love—infinitely more significant than brute force, there is something—wisdom —infinitely more significant than mental prowess. A remarkably developed intelligence impresses us about as much as a sixteen-inch biceps. If we know anything, we know that a lot of people can learn knowledge (which is the same thing as unlearning ignorance) but that no one can learn wisdom. Wisdom, like love, is a spiritual gift. And Krazy happens to be extraordinarily gifted. She has not only the gift of love, but the gift of wisdom as well. Her unknowledgeable wisdom blossoms in almost every episode of our meteoric burlesk melodrama; the supreme blossom, perhaps, being a tribute to Offissa Pupp and Ignatz Mouse— who (as she observes) are playing a little game together. Right! The game they're playing, willy nilly, is the exciting democratic game of *cat loves mouse,* the game which a lot of highly moral people all over the so-called world consider uncivilized. I refer (of course) to those

red-brown-and-black-shirted Puritans who want us all to scrap democracy and adopt their modernized version of *follow the leader*—a strictly ultraprogressive and superbenevolent affair which begins with the liquidation of Ignatz Mouse by Offissa Pupp. But (objects Krazy, in her innocent democratic way) Ignatz Mouse and Offissa Pupp are having fun. Right again! And—from the Puritan point of view—nothing could be worse. Fun, to Puritans, is something wicked: an invention of The Devil Himself. That's why all these superbenevolent collectivists are so hyperspinelessly keen on having us play their ultraprogressive game. The first superbenevolent rule of their ultraprogressive game is *thou shalt not play*.

If only the devilish game of democracy were exclusively concerned with such mindful matters as ignorance and knowledge, crime and punishment, cruelty and kindness, collectivists would really have something on the ball. But it so happens that democracy involves the spiritual values of wisdom, love, and joy. Democracy isn't democracy because or although Ignatz Mouse and Offissa Pupp are fighting a peaceful war. Democracy is democracy insofar as our villain and our hero—by having their fun, by playing their brutal little game—happen (despite their worst and best efforts) to be fulfilling our heroine's immeasurable destiny. Joy is her destiny: and joy comes through Ignatz—via Offissa Pupp; since it's our villain's loathing for law which gives him the strength of ten when he hurls his blissyielding brick. Let's not forget that. And let's be perfectly sure about something else. Even if Offissa Pupp should go crazy and start chasing Krazy, and even if Krazy

should go crazy and start chasing Ignatz, and even if crazy Krazy should swallow crazy Ignatz and crazy Offissa Pupp should swallow crazy Krazy and it was the millennium—there'd still be the brick. And (having nothing else to swallow) Offissa Pupp would then swallow the brick. Whereupon, as the brick hit Krazy, Krazy would be happy.

Alas for sensical reformers! Never can they realize that penguins do fly; that Krazy's idiocy and helplessness in terms of a world—any world—are as nothing to the nth power, by comparison with a world's—any world's—helplessness and idiocy in terms of Krazy. Yet the truth of truths lies here and nowhere else. Always (no matter what's real) Krazy is no mere reality. She is a living ideal. She is a spiritual force, inhabiting a merely real world—and the realer a merely real world happens to be, the more this living ideal becomes herself. Hence—needless to add —the brick. Only if, and whenever, that kind reality (cruelly wielded by our heroic villain, Ignatz Mouse, in despite of our villainous hero, Offissa Pupp) smites Krazy—fairly and squarely —does the joyous symbol of Love Fulfilled appear above our triumphantly unknowledgeable heroine. And now do we understand the meaning of democracy? If we don't, a poet-painter called George Herriman most certainly cannot be blamed. Democracy, he tells us again and again and again, isn't some ultraprogressive myth of a superbenevolent World As Should Be. The meteoric burlesk melodrama of democracy is a struggle between society (Offissa Pupp) and the individual (Ignatz Mouse) over an ideal (our heroine)—a struggle from which, again and again and again, emerges one stupendous fact:

namely, that the ideal of democracy fulfills herself only if, and whenever, society fails to suppress the individual.

Could anything possibly be clearer?

Nothing—unless it's the kindred fact that our illimitably affectionate Krazy has no connection with the old-fashioned heroine of common or garden melodrama. The prosaically "virtuous" puppet couldn't bat a decorously "innocent" eyelash without immediately provoking some utterly estimable Mr. Righto to liquidate some perfectly wicked Mr. Wrongo. In her hyperspineless puritanical simplicity, she desired nothing quite so much as an ultraprogressive and superbenevolent substitute for human nature. Democracy's merciful leading lady, on the other hand, is a fundamentally complex being who demands the whole mystery of life. Krazy Kat—who, with every mangled word and murdered gesture, translates a mangling and murdering world into Peace And Goodwill— is the only original and authentic revolutionary protagonist. All blood-and-thunder Worlds As Should Be cannot comprise this immeasurably generous heroine of the strictly unmitigated future.

She has no fear—even of a mouse.

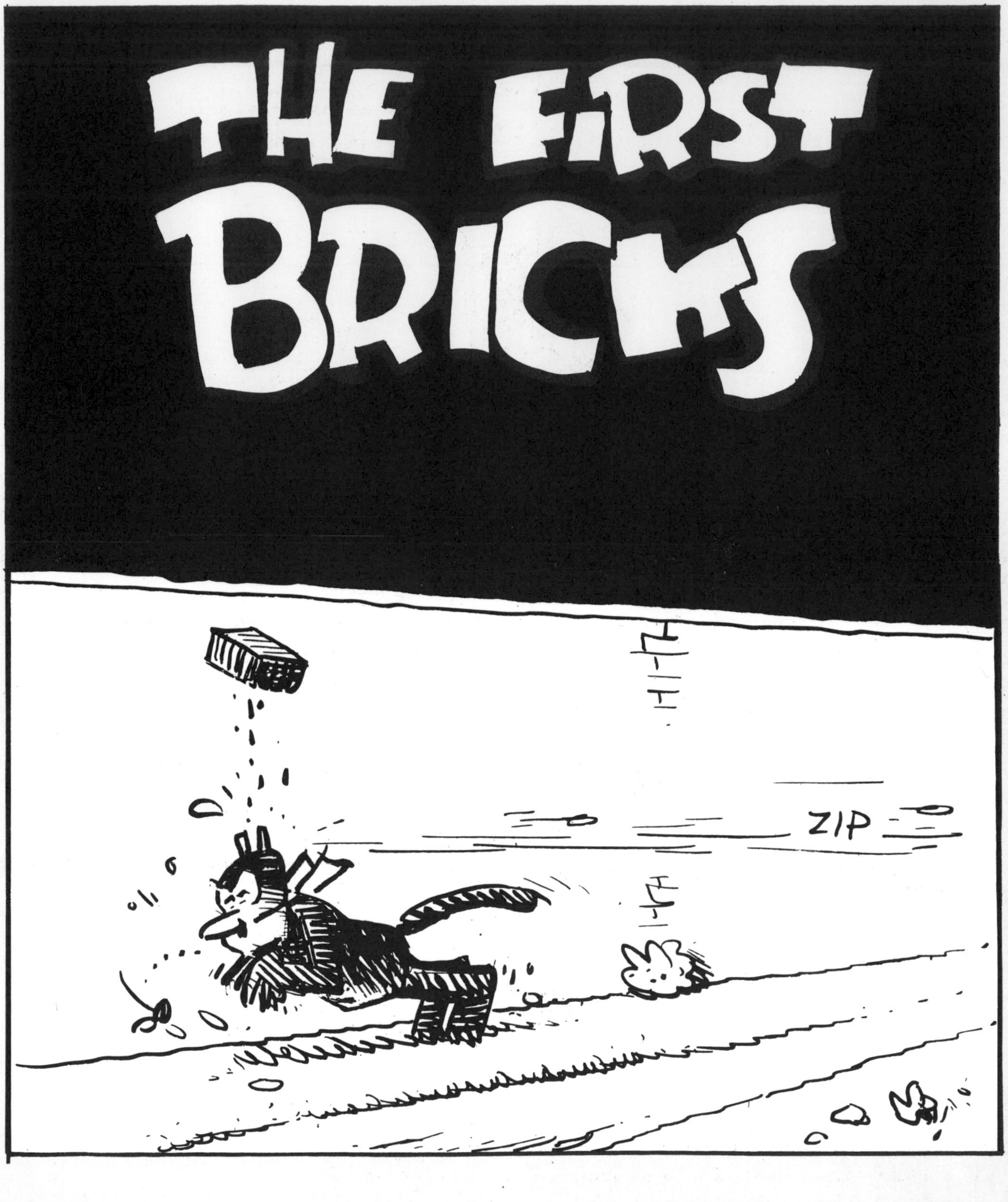
THE FIRST BRICKS
ZIP

The Family Upstairs

About 1909 the first "inklings" of the genius that was George Herriman began to appear in his DINGBAT FAMILY strip. Popping up amongst the panels came a family cat and with it a mouse. Two years later the cat and mouse were enjoying themselves in a little strip running under the Dingbats. These early signs of creativity are reprinted for the first time.

18

In a short while the doings of the cat and mouse began to become more and more important. As a matter of fact the DINGBAT FAMILY began to get involved with them. The following 11 pages show examples of KRAZY KAT while it was still running under the DINGBAT FAMILY.

The Early Strips 1911-1912

The Early Strips 1911-1912

The Early Strips 1911-1912

The Early Strips 1911-1912

The Early Strips   1911-1912

The Early Strips 1911-1912

FLIGHTS OF FANCY

While humor is the main ingredient in the funnies, Herriman often went beyond it in KRAZY KAT. Every so often Krazy would give out with poetic statements or relate fables of rare warmth and charm. What is even more amazing is that Herriman was able to match this mood exactly with his art. Here was a world of fantasy that few artists, writers or poets ever were able to manage. Yet one man was able to do it...and in a comic strip!

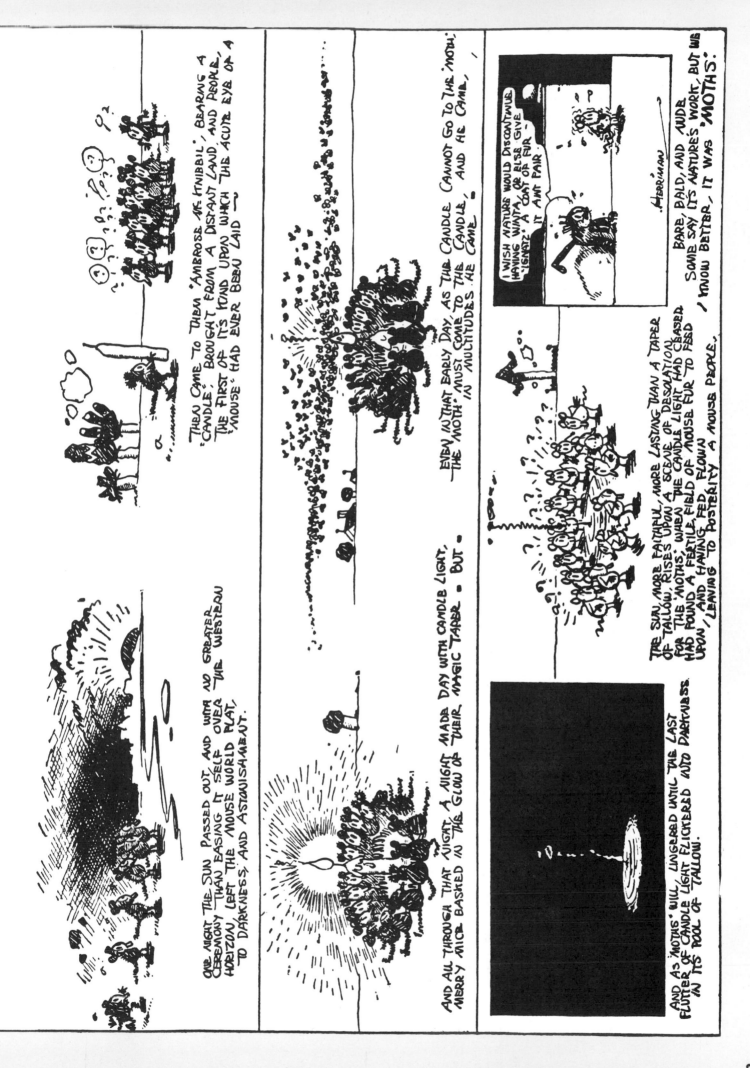

THEN CAME TO THEM "AMBROSE AF KNIBBL", BEARING A "CANDLE", BROUGHT FROM A DISTANT LAND AND PEOPLE, THE FIRST OF IT'S KIND UPON WHICH THE ACUTE EYE OF A "MOUSE" HAD EVER BEEN LAID —

ONE NIGHT THE SUN PASSED OUT AND WITH NO GREATER CEREMONY THAN EASING IT SELF OVER THE WESTERN HORIZON, LEFT THE MOUSE WORLD FLAT, TO DARKNESS, AND ASTONISHMENT.

EVEN IN THAT EARLY DAY, AS THE CANDLE CANNOT GO TO THE "MOTH", THE "MOTH" MUST COME TO THE CANDLE, AND HE CAME, IN MULTITUDES, HE CAME,

AND ALL THROUGH THAT NIGHT A NIGHT MADE DAY WITH CANDLE LIGHT, MERRY MICE BASKED IN THE GLOW OF THEIR MAGIC TAPER - BUT -

THE SUN, MORE FAITHFUL, MORE LASTING THAN A TAPER OF TALLOW, RISES UPON A SCENE OF DESOLATION, FOR THE "MOTHS", WHEN THE CANDLE LIGHT HAD CEASED HAD FOUND A FERTILE FIELD OF MOUSE FUR TO FEED UPON, AND HAVING FED FLOWN / LEAVING TO POSTERITY A MOUSE PEOPLE.

I WISH NATURE WOULD DISCONTINUE HAVING WINTA, OR ELSE GIVE "IGNATZ" A COAT OR FUR - IT AINT FAIR.

HERRIMAN

BARE, BALD, AND NUDE SOME SAY IT'S NATURE'S WORK, BUT WE / KNOW BETTER - IT WAS "MOTHS".

AND AS "MOTHS" WILL LINGERED UNTIL THE LAST FLUTTER OF CANDLE LIGHT FLICKERED INTO DARKNESS, IN ITS POOL OF TALLOW.

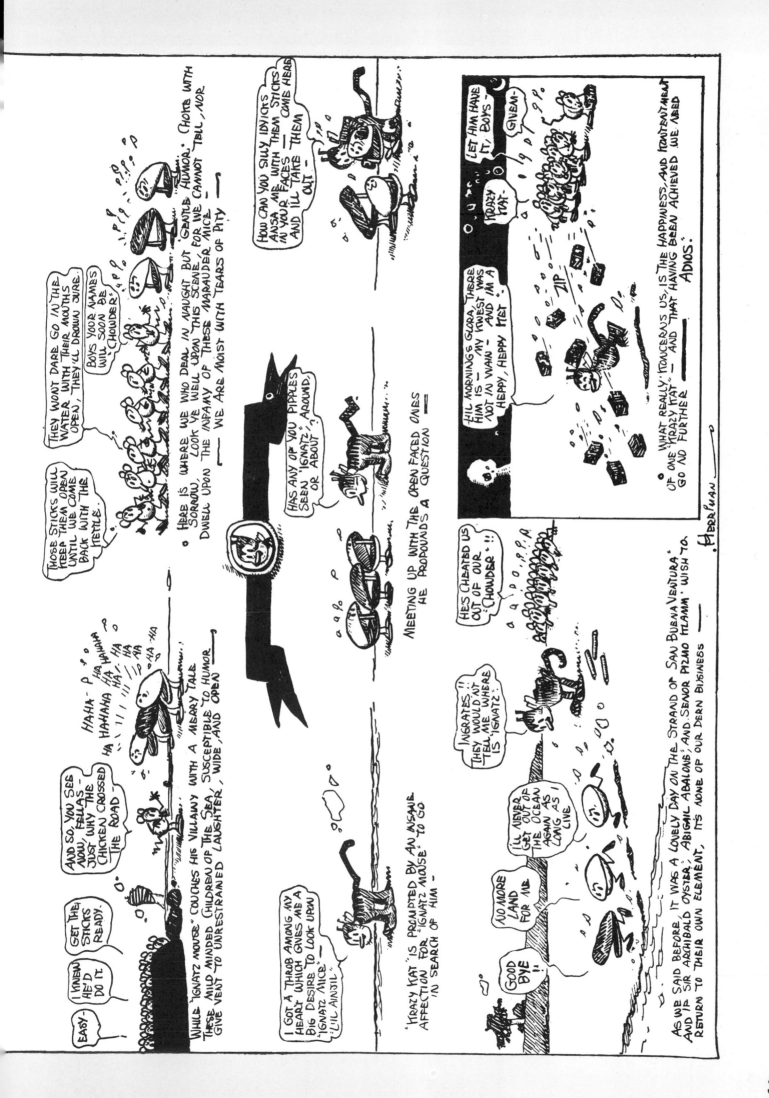

37

Flights of Fancy

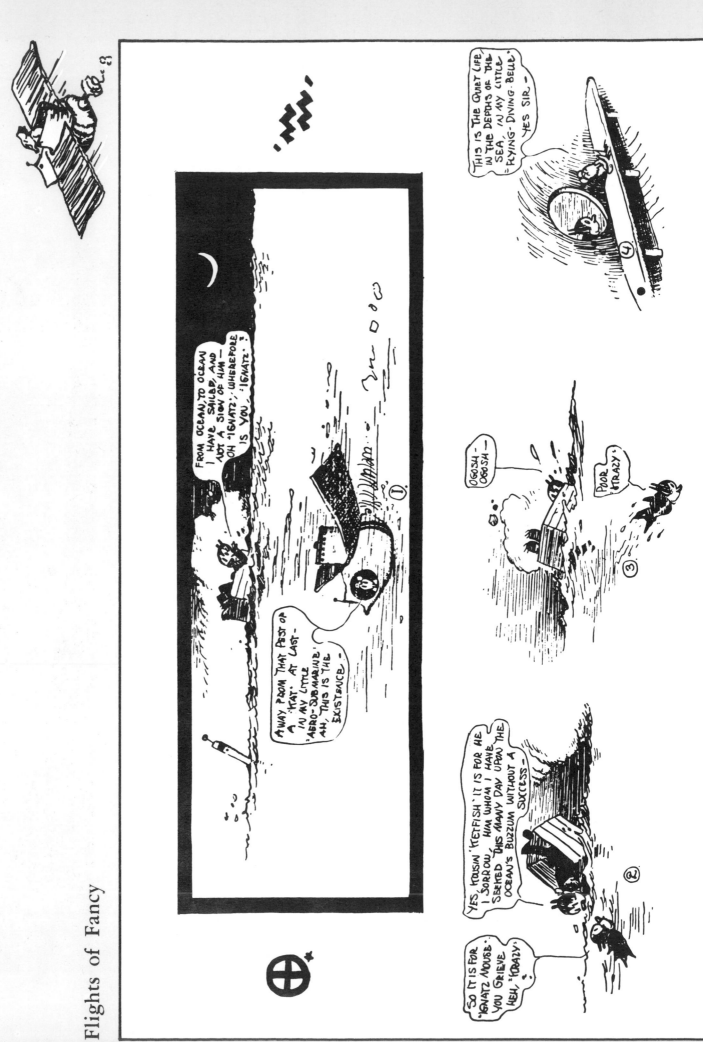

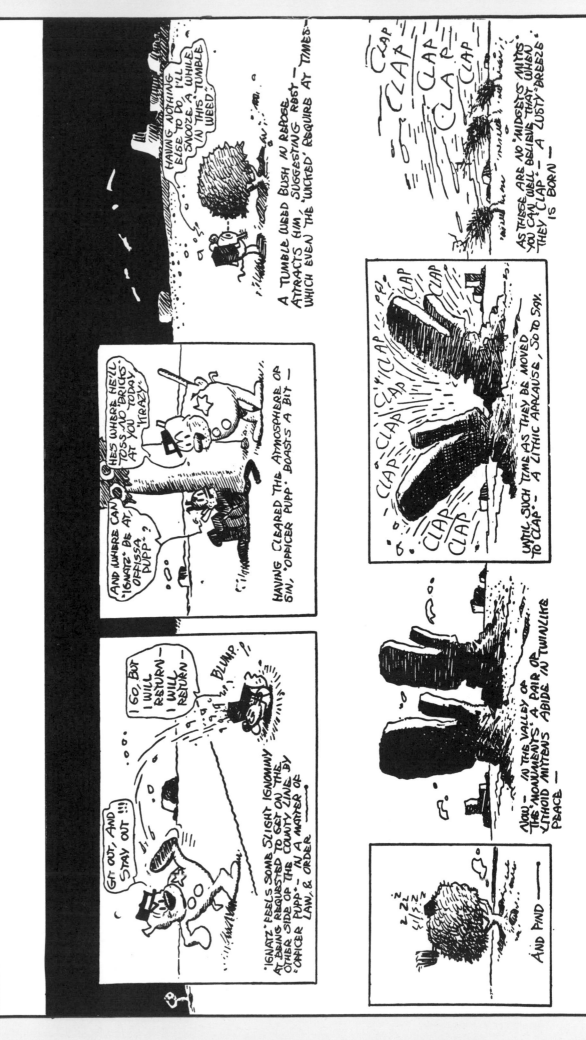

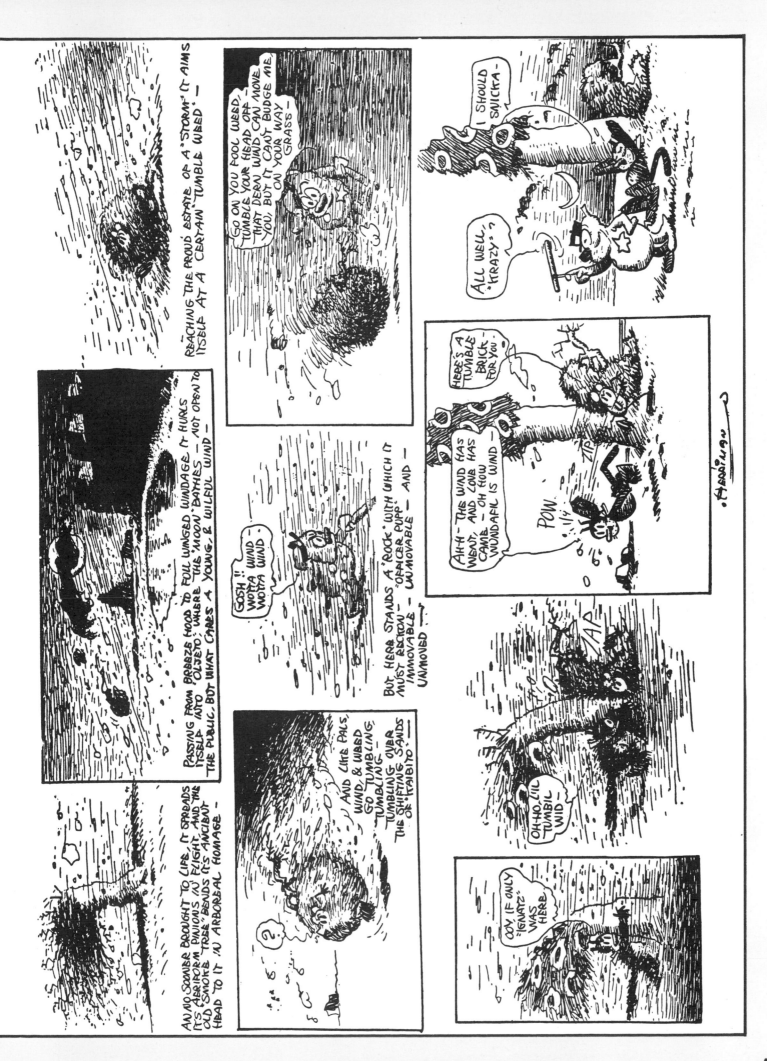

43

MANY THINGS HAVE STALKED THROUGH "COCONINO", AND YET HAVE LEFT BUT LITTLE IMPRESS UPON THAT ASTUTE DEMOCRATIC COMMUNITY - BUT YESTERDAY, ROYALTY, IN THE SHAPE OF A "KING" STRUTTED INTO THEIR MIDST, AND EVERY SOUL AMONG THEM WAS SHAKEN TO ITS VERY CENTER.

"KOLIN KELLY" DEALER IN BRICKS, NO LONGER ATTIRES HIMSELF IN THE EMBLEM OF TRUE REPUBLICANISM THE "BINOCLE", SINCE HIS ATTACHMENT TO THE KING'S PERSON AS CUSTODIAN OF THE IMPERIAL BRICK, HE NOW BASKS IN THE SHEEN OF ROYALTY WITH HIS EYE DECKED OUT IN A SET OF ONE CYLINDER CHEATERS, THE "MONOCLE".

"MOCK DUCK" NO LONGER DEALS WITH THE PROLETARIAT, BEING NOW THE ROYAL LAUNDRABER, AND SHIRT MANGLER TO HIS MAJESTY -

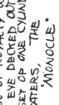

"KRISTOPHER KRACKL", ONCE LEADER OF THE POPULIST TICKET, LETS IT BE KNOWN THAT HE IS NOW IN THE KING'S GOOD GRACES, HAVING BEEN MADE LORD HIGH BREAKFAST ANNOUNCER, AND IMPERIAL KAROO TO THE KOURT -

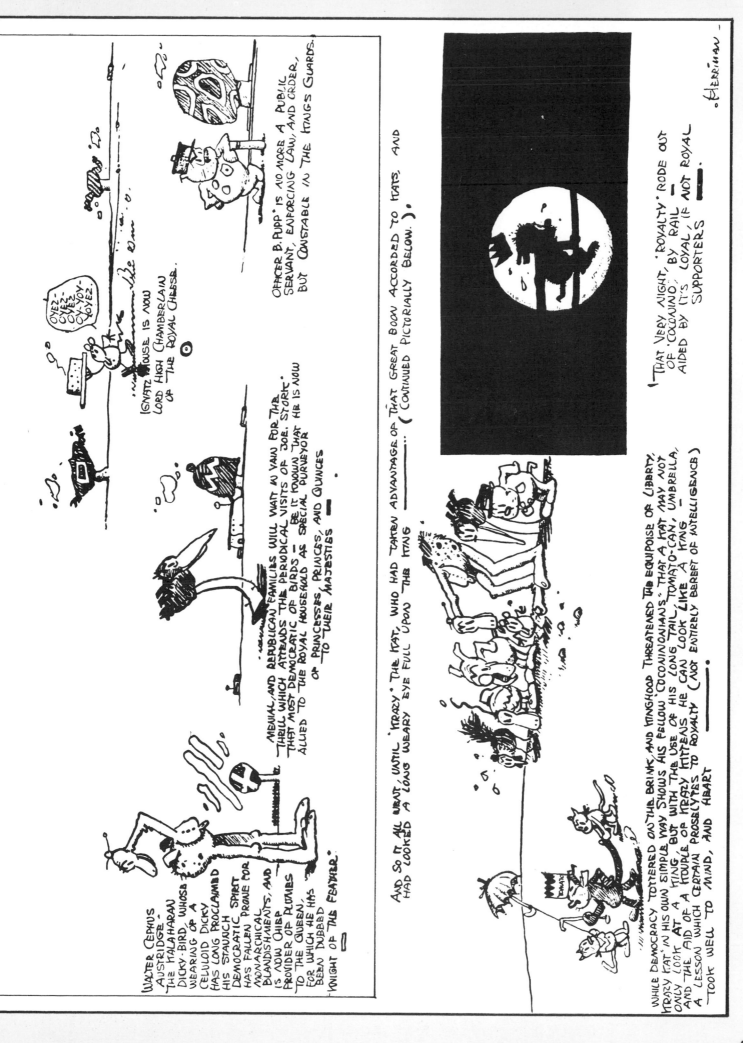

WALTER CEPHUS
AUSTRIDGE—
THE KALAHARAN
DICKY·BIRD, WHOSE
WEARING OF A
CELULOID DICKY
HAS LONG PROCLAIMED
HIS STAUNCH
DEMOCRATIC SPIRIT
HAS FALLEN PRONE FOR
MONARCHICAL
BLANDISHMENTS AND
IS NOW CHIEF
PROVIDER OF PLUMES
TO THE QUEEN,
FOR WHICH HE HAS
BEEN DUBBED
"KNIGHT OF THE FEATHER."

IGNATZ MOUSE IS NOW
LORD HIGH CHAMBERLAIN
OF THE ROYAL CHEESE.

OYEZ-
OYEZ-
OYEZ-
O-YOY-
YOYEZ.

OFFICER B. PUPP" IS NO MORE A PUBLIC
SERVANT, ENFORCING LAW, AND ORDER,
BUT CONSTABLE IN THE KING'S GUARDS.

MENIAL AND REPUBLICAN FAMILIES WILL WAIT IN VAIN FOR THE
THRILL WHICH ATTENDS THE PERIODICAL VISITS OF JOE. STORK—
THAT MOST DEMOCRATIC OF BIRDS— BE IT KNOWN THAT HE IS NOW
ALLIED TO THE ROYAL HOUSEHOLD AS SPECIAL PURVEYOR
OF PRINCESSES, PRINCES, AND QUINCES
TO THEIR MAJESTIES.

AND SO IT ALL WENT, UNTIL "KRAZY" THE KAT, WHO HAD TAKEN ADVANTAGE OF THAT GREAT BOON ACCORDED TO KATS, AND
HAD LOOKED A LONG WEARY EYE FULL UPON THE KING ———— (CONTINUED PICTORIALLY BELOW.).

"THAT VERY NIGHT, "ROYALTY" RODE OUT
OF "COCONINO," BY RAIL
AIDED BY IT'S LOYAL, IF NOT ROYAL
SUPPORTERS ————

-Herriman-

WHILE DEMOCRACY TOTTERED ON THE BRINK, AND KINGHOOD THREATENED THE EQUIPOISE OF LIBERTY,
KRAZY KAT IN HIS OWN SIMPLE WAY SHOWS HIS FELLOW COCONINOANIANS- THAT A KAT MAY NOT
ONLY LOOK AT A KING, BUT WITH THE USE OF HIS LONG TAIL, TOMATO-CAN, UMBRELLA,
AND THE AID OF A KOUPLE OF KRAZY KITTENS HE CAN LOOK LIKE A KING
A LESSON WHICH CERTAIN PROSELYTES TO ROYALTY (NOT ENTIRELY BEREFT OF INTELLIGENCE)
TOOK WELL TO MIND, AND APART ————.

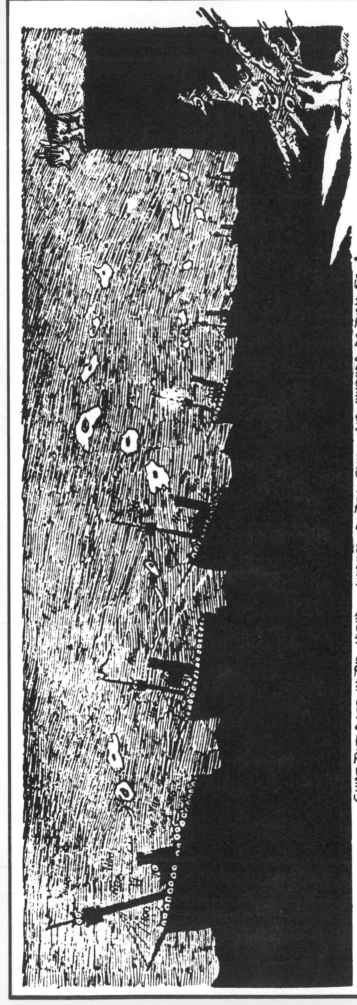

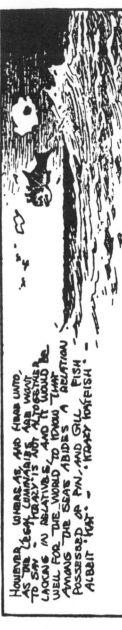

SHIPS THAT PASS IN THE NIGHT - WHENCE DO THEY COME, AND WHITHER DO THEY GO - AND SO, "KURIOSITY" IS BORN IN THE PALPITATING BOSOM OF "KRAZY KAT". "KURIOSITY" UNREQUITED - AND UNSATISFIED AS THE OBJECTS OF HIS INQUISITIVENESS LIE IN AN ELEMENT FORBIDDEN TO KATS - QUANTITIES OF OCEAN, MULTITUDES OF WATER.

HOWEVER, WHEREAS, AND FIRAB UNTO, AS THE "OCEAN LUMINARIES" ARE WONT TO SAY - "KRAZY" IS NOT ALTOGETHER LACKING IN RELATIVES, AND IT WOULD BE WELL FOR THE WORLD TO KNOW THAT AMONG THE SEAS ABIDES A RELATION - POSSESSED OF FIN, AND GILL, FISH ALBEIT "KAT" - "KRAZY KATFISH" -

SHIPS, WHETHER THEY BE OF NOCTURNAL, OR DIURNAL PASSAGE MUST SAIL THE SEAS, AN ELEMENT UNFAVORABLE TO KATS - WHICH MAKES IT LOOK AS IF KRAZY'S KURIOSITY MUST GO UNAPPEASED —

© 1928 by Int'l Feature Service, Inc   Great Britain rights reserved.

1-15

It started centuries ago when a Roman mouse fell in love with an Egyptian cat. His adoring words were sent to her written on the side of a brick. Eons later Ignatz Mouse still sent bricks to Krazy but now only she understood them. Somewhere only the years Offisa Pupp popped up and lost his heart to Krazy. Thus George Herriman gave birth to a love triangle bound by a brick.

Stop! Look! . . . An'??

Camouflage Capers!

Ignatz out of range.

"Ignatz-Angelo" he ain't!

Sail on, little brick!

Rubber Repercussions!

Getting "stuck" with it?

The latest model brick!

"Free-wheelin' " bricks?

Buttered or plain, Dollink?

Dark endeavors.

Herriman

Wall, wall! Fency dat!

Some you win, but then again . . .

Put a curve on it!

More curve play!

Will wonders never cease!?

COPR. 1944, KING FEATURES SYNDICATE, Inc. WORLD RIGHTS RESERVED

Playing into the hands of fate!

Ever vigilant! And alert too!

Double your pleasure! Double your fun!

Home remedies, anyone?

"Chute" the works!

He obeys the law, he does!

A good skate!

Playin' a "baitin'" game, eh?

The innocent makes a comeback!

KOLOR IT KRAZY

Color was no stranger to George Herriman. He had been using it in Sunday strips as early as 1901. But it really wasn't a necessary thing for Krazy Kat. The art and humor carried it all. Still Herriman used it to its fullest and added scope and dimension where perfection already existed.

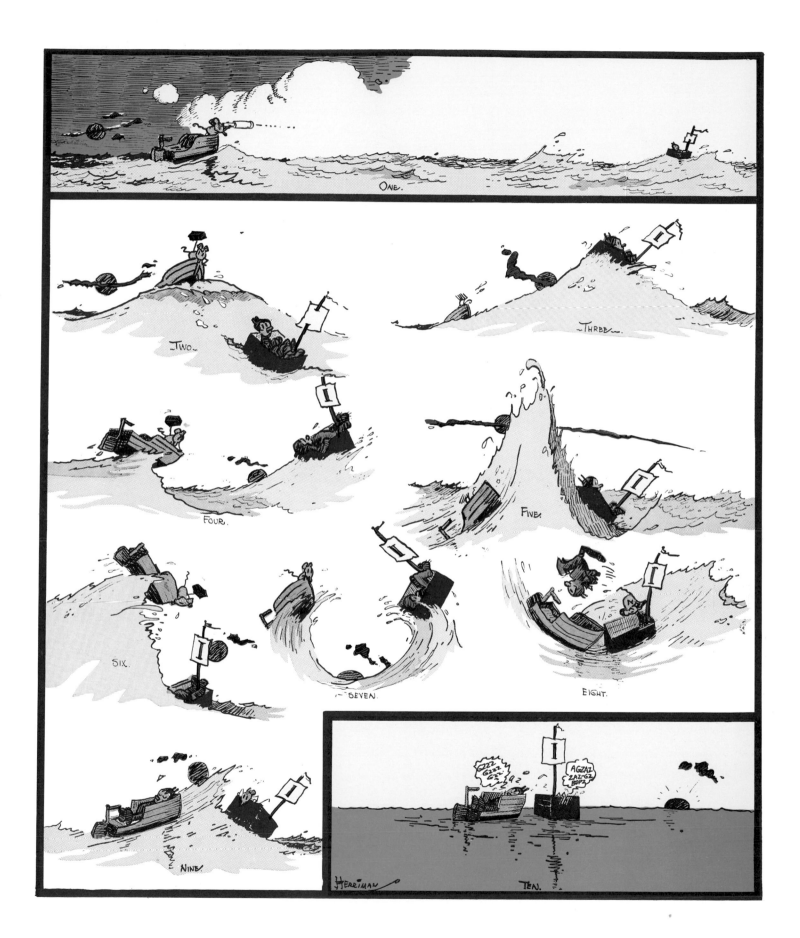

Copr. 1942, King Features Syndicate, Inc., World rights reserved.

A TALE OF TIGER TEA

Continuity was nothing alien to the KRAZY KAT strip. Often episodes were run that lasted for weeks and months. But in June of 1936, George Herriman sent Krazy off on a quest. When the Kat returned, Coconino County was never quite the same for two years. For with the Kat came a bag of Tiger Tea . . . and herein lies only part of the tale that follows.

A Tale of Tiger Tea

100

COCONINO COUNTY LAUGH-IN

When George Herriman went off on a tangent, readers of Krazy Kat got it socked to them. They groaned, moaned and laughed over it. It was day after day of blackouts that floored readers with outrageous puns and gags. But still it had a quality that separated it from other strips and the readers knew it.

FRIJULES

Losing their collective minds!

It was printed on flypaper!

Now you see him, now you . . .

Sock it to 'im! Sock it to 'im!

Up! Down? Up? Down! ?!

Using his invisible brain, he is!

There'll be a hot time!

Collar this one if you can!

Which is which???

Sipprize is right!

"Watch" this!!

GIVE ME THE GOOD OLD DAYS... I THINK!?

The world may change but the people in it forever remain the same. Today, some thirty or more years after these strips first appeared, they apply, and are pertinent, to events taking place in the world around us. The one test of true art is that it stands the test of time. That's why Krazy Kat can still pack a punch.

Remember, remember!

Give me my rights!

Copr. 1942, King Features Syndicate, Inc., World rights reserved. 8-2

124

" _____ "

Keep our cities clean, hear!

126

The patriots?!?

Lunar-Nutts!!

Moon shot! That's right, shot!

You don't smoke katnip, or do you???

How do you pay a telepathy bill?

Do the spirits lie?

Sending out peace feelers!

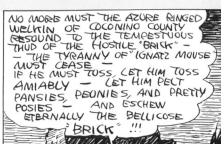

Rebelling under an alias!

Oh, those rebels!

Youth, oh, beautiful youth??

Table turning doesn't work!

Registered U. S. Patent Office.

© 1941 King Features Syndicate, Inc., World rights reserved

Bypassing legal barriers...

Justice's blind, not deaf!

The pursuit of liberty. (The chase is on!)

Friends of freedom.

The hound of justice.

We protest, we picket and . . .

Do your thing, baby!

Let it all hang out!

Natural child for sure!

Do it now, the future can wait!

George Herriman had a love for music. When he courted Mrs. Herriman in the late 1890's, he would serenade her while he strummed his mandolin. Often throughout the thirty-four year run of the KRAZY KAT strip, music would appear in the panels. It could be raucous or sweet. But whatever the melody, the troubadour known as Krazy always ended on a happy note.

One, two, three . . . Now all together!

Not always what it seems, it seems!

Do they sell literal licenses?

Fate twice tempted!

Strange . . . but classical!

Hide'n Seek, musical style!

Music with green eyes???

Offisa Pupp knows his notes!

162

It takes all kinds to make music!

Not much hidden meaning here!

Love has many, many meanings!

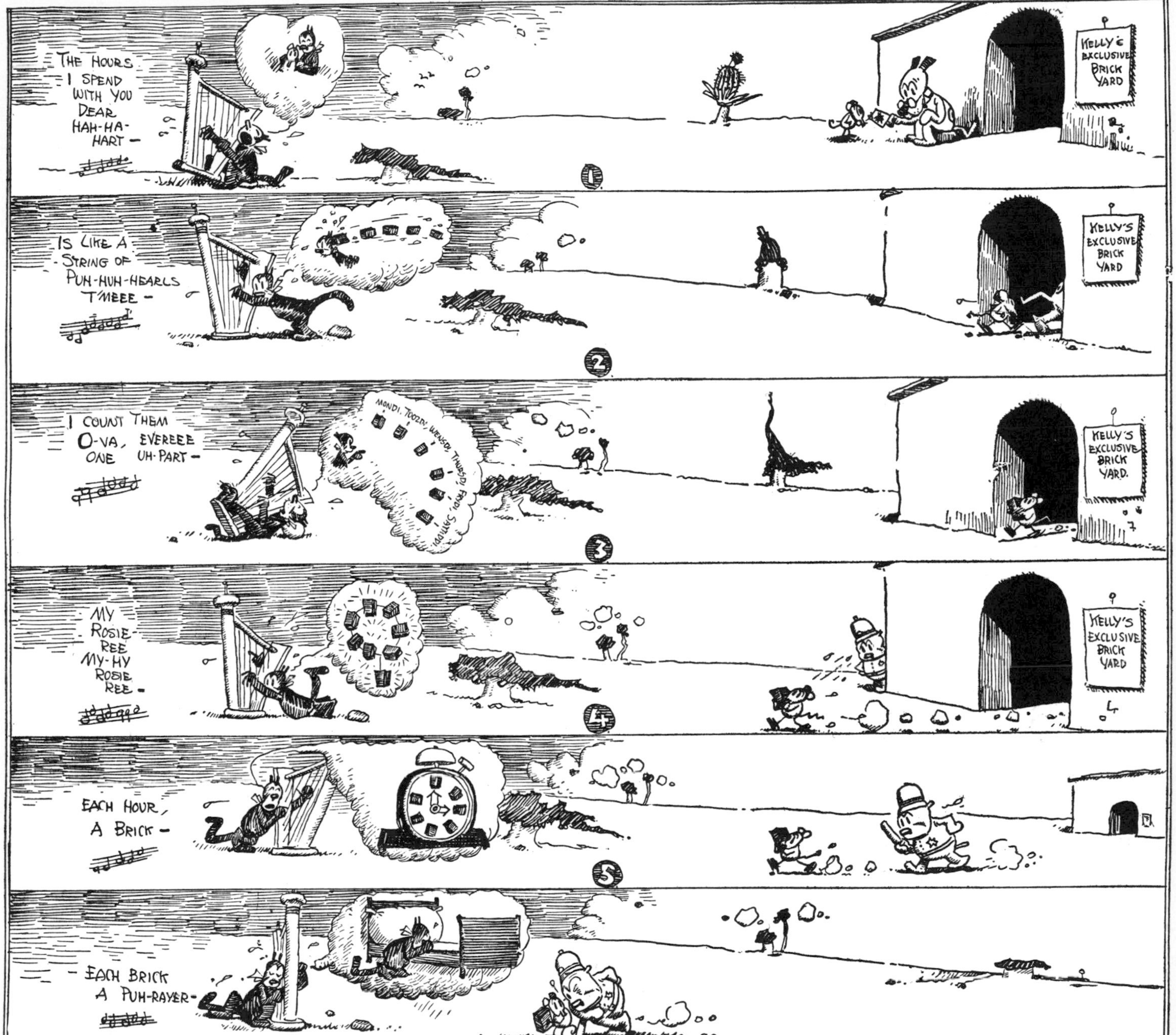

Look!! We've struck logic!

Ending on a HEPPY note!

You have written truth, you friends
of the "shadows", yet be not
    harsh with "Krazy".
He is but a shadow himself,
caught in the web of
    this mortal skein.
We call him "cat",
We call him "crazy"
        yet is he neither.
At some time will he ride away
to you, people of the twilight,
his password will be the echoes of
a vesper bell, his coach, a
zephyr from the west
        forgive him, for you will
understand him no better than we
    who linger on this side of
        the pale.